Muddy Waters
Hamish and the Falkirk Wheel

I'M ONLY SMALL, AND SOMETIMES TINY. I'M ON EVERY PAGE, CAN YOU FIND ME?

Hamish and the Falkirk Wheel

It was some time since the Thrupp boats had seen their old friend Hamish. He lived far away in Scotland. The boats knew his long trips were always full of adventures. Jolly Boatman was very excited about meeting Hamish. The story of Hamish's battle with the Loch Ness Monster had been told many times, but no-one was really sure whether it was true.

Now Hamish had a new tale to tell. He'd helped to build the amazing Falkirk Wheel and he wanted everyone to know about it.

Arriving early that summer morning, Hamish found the Thrupp boats fast asleep. He decided it was time they were busy. He quietly puttered up to Cedric the dredger, who was snoring loudly at his berth and said in a loud voice, 'Wake up, laddie! There's work to do, and you're the boat that should be doing it.' Cedric woke with a start and frowned at Hamish, who chuckled as he went to greet the other boats.

'Och, it's braw to see ye again, pal,' Hamish said to Muddy Waters.
'It's been far too long, Hamish. Are you still carrying cargo?' asked Muddy.
'Oh aye, I'll be carrying for many a year to come. It's what keeps me so strong and fit. Well, who's this smart young fellow?'

Jolly was wide-eyed. He'd never seen such a colourful and unusual boat as Hamish before. He couldn't help staring at Hamish's hull.
'Oh you're interested in my scars are you? Nessie left these when I visited her loch. They're all healed now, but it was quite a battle.'
So it *is* true. Hamish really did fight with the Loch Ness Monster, thought Jolly.

'I can't stay long, Muddy, as I have to get back for the Falkirk Wheel celebrations. Some of the world's biggest barges are coming up and I have to be there.'

Muddy had always wanted to see the new wheel. Some boats didn't believe such a huge lock could exist.

'Can we go back with Hamish?' asked Jolly quietly.

To his surprise and delight, he saw Muddy break into a wide smile. 'Why ever not, it's about time you saw the wonders of the north. Would you be happy to have us along with you?' Muddy asked Hamish.

'Och aye, I'll be glad of your company and you can tell all yer pals about our wonderful wheel,' he said proudly.

'There's no such thing as the Falkirk Wheel!' shouted Cedric across the wharf. 'Everyone knows it's another one of Hamish's tall tales.'

'Well, *I* believe it and I can't wait to prove you wrong!' shouted Jolly defiantly.

The journey to Scotland was a great adventure. Jolly enjoyed the thrill of visiting so many new places, but he found passing through the longer flights of locks very tiring indeed. He wished there was an easier way to go up and down on the waterways.

Hamish laughed as he watched Jolly huff and puff his way through the locks. He couldn't wait to show the little narrowboat just how easy it would be on the Falkirk Wheel. But Muddy had a very special surprise to show Jolly before they left England.

Manchester Milly was waiting with the warmest of welcomes, as the three friends arrived at the Anderton Boat Lift. Milly was proud to tell Jolly all about the history of the lift and that it was over one hundred years old. Jolly looked up in amazement.

'Wow! It's huge,' said an overawed Jolly.
'Huge!' boomed Hamish. 'That's not huge. The Falkirk Wheel is more than twice as big and much faster.'
'Now, now, Hamish,' chuckled Muddy, 'there's no need to show off. After all, this lift has been around even longer than you!'

They all thanked Milly for looking after them and invited her to visit Thrupp very soon.

'Come on, wee fella, there's something I think you should see,' whispered an excited Hamish. Blinking through the mist of the cold morning air, Jolly and Muddy watched in wonder as the outline of something enormous emerged before them.
'Here she is boys, the greatest canal lift you're ever likely to see!' beamed Hamish with pride.

Muddy Waters let out a long appreciative whistle, but Jolly Boatman was utterly speechless. Towering above them was the Falkirk Wheel, the biggest lock ever built on a British waterway.

Eventually, Jolly muttered, 'I *knew* it was true.'
'Och aye, laddie, and you're about to find out just how it works!' said Hamish. He ushered Jolly and Muddy over to the lifting gate and urged them to follow him in.

Muddy Waters could see that Jolly was nervous and reluctant to go, so he gave him a reassuring wink and a nudge forward.

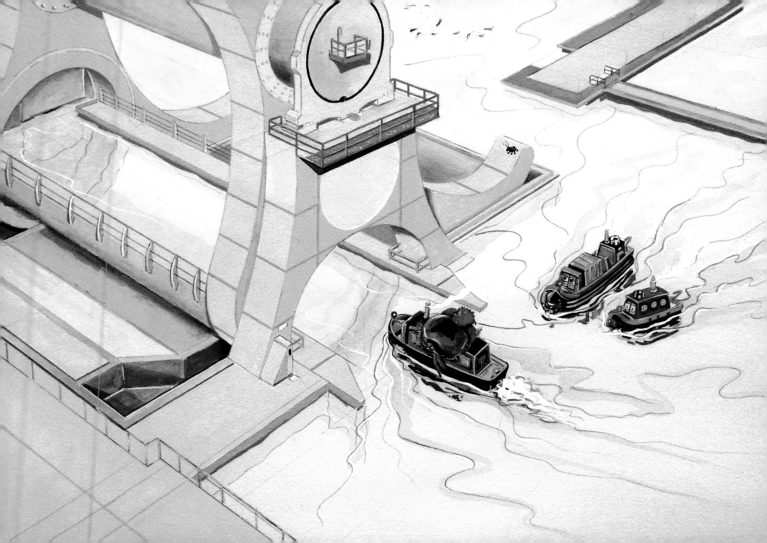

'I can't do it, Muddy! It's too big, and too high, and too..., too scary!' he shouted.

'Alright, calm down little fellow,' said Muddy as he backed away from the gate. 'We will watch Hamish go first and then see some local boats come back down too. Then you'll see that it's safe and not at all frightening. I have a very strong feeling that you will really enjoy this.'

Jolly wasn't so sure, as he watched the enormous wheel turn slowly before his ever widening eyes.

Muddy and Jolly watched Hamish rise up into the sky until they could no longer see him. Then they waited and saw other boats come back down. All of them appeared excited as they chatted to one another.

'You see,' said a confident Muddy Waters, 'there really isn't anything to worry about. It's our turn to go up.'
This wheel might have replaced eleven exhausting locks thought Jolly, but right now I know which I would prefer.

Jolly closed his eyes tightly as he entered the gate. '*There's nothing to be afraid of, there's nothing to be afraid of,*' he muttered to himself over and over again.

As the lift reached the half way stage, he briefly opened his eyes. He had never been so high! He thought he might be dizzy, or fall over the edge, but he was too excited. Below, he could see the far off rolling Scottish countryside with its tiny canals and waterways. It was too fantastic to be scared.

Arriving at the top of the wheel, the two Oxfordshire boats were met by a happy Hamish. 'You're the bravest wee boat on the whole of the Union canal,' he told Jolly kindly.

'I knew there was nothing to be frightened of when I saw *you* do it, Hamish.' said a proud Jolly Boatman. 'Everything looked so tiny from up there in the sky and it was so much easier than going through lots of locks, he added excitedly.

Having risen through the clouds, Jolly now felt brave enough for anything. This was a good job, because Hamish had another surprise in store. 'I needed to know if you were ready to come with me to Loch Ness, young fella,' said Hamish.
Jolly gulped and glanced at Hamish's teeth marks. 'Right now, I feel on top of the world, and not even Nessie herself could scare me!' he yelled.

They all laughed as they headed off to their next big adventure on the Caledonian Canal.

Who is Muddy Waters?

Muddy Waters is no ordinary narrowboat as you'll discover in this exciting new series of stories. Set in well known and loved locations throughout Britain's beautiful waterways, you'll soon become familiar with such colourful characters as Dizzy Spells, Cedric, Dawn Chorus, Dudley and the rest of Muddy's buddies. Muddy invites you to find out so much more at

www.muddywaters.org.uk

Glossary

Berth: a special place at a wharf where boats can rest

Cargo: things like wood and coal carried from place to place by the boats

Hull: the main part of a boat, including the bottom, sides and deck

Loch: the Scottish name for a lake

Barges: long flat-bottomed boats for carrying cargo on canals or rivers

Lock: gates on the canal which can be opened or closed to change the water level. Then boats can be raised or lowered as they travel through hills and valleys. A **flight of locks** is where there are many locks close together

Wharf: a place where boats can stop to load and unload their cargo and where they can stay for a while

Narrowboat: a canal boat less than 2.1 metres wide that is steered with a tiller not a wheel

Lift: a boat lift is a machine for transporting boats between water at two different levels

Titles Out Now...

Poppy at the Boat Show

Pearly's Welcome to London

Jolly Boatman's Lesson

Coming Soon

Ol' One Eye's Revenge

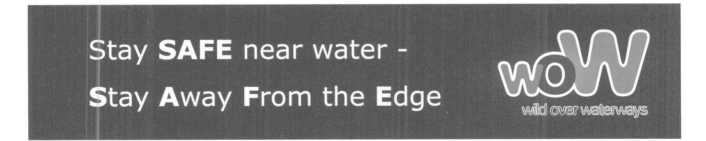

Stay **SAFE** near water -
Stay **A**way **F**rom the **E**dge

woW
wild over waterways

Go Wild Over Waterways - find games, learning and fun things to do at www.wow4water.net